RSVP: The Directory of Illustration and Design is published by Richard Lebenson and Kathleen Creighton, P.O. Box 050314, Brooklyn, NY 11205. None of the artwork in this book may be reproduced in any manner without written permission from the individual artist. ©2005 Richard Lebenson. All rights reserved 2005. Volume 30, number 1
ISBN 1-878118-14-5
Printed in China

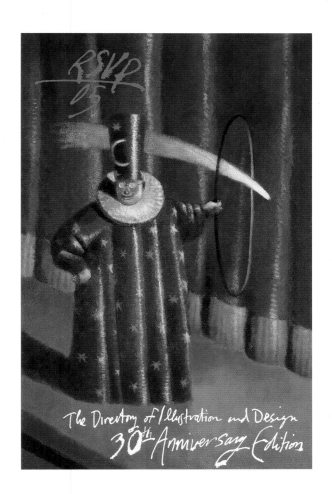

The Directory of Illustration and Design
30th Anniversary Edition

Thank You

On this special occasion, *our 30th Anniversary Edition*, we would like to take the opportunity to thank all the people who made it possible. We couldn't have done it, certainly not with the level of class and quality that we're known for, without their help.

First and foremost the staff of RSVP deserves a large amount of credit for our success. Kathleen Creighton, Co-Publisher, Joe Greenstein, Business Manager, Frank Attong, Distribution/Sales/Traffic, Harvey Wilson, Mailing List and Paul Krauss, Sales. Other people who have been of enormous help over the years are Stephen Bodkin of Bodkin Creative and Emma Crawford, both of whom have worked with us from everything from promotion to design and typesetting. John Cleveland and Marc Weinstein also deserve a special mention.

We've been lucky to work with some special people in the printing business as well. Steve Wayne of Wayne Graphics/Toledo, Ohio; Gary Stahl of Lanman/Washington, D.C. and Fleetwood Litho/NY & NJ; Bob Dimino of L.P. Thebault/NJ; George Dick and the staff of Four Colour Imports, including Nancy Heinonen and Martha Burton; Ken Chung, Tom & Mary Chung, Frankie, Hong and all the pressmen and production people at Everbest/Hong Kong & China.

We certainly owe a great deal to all of our cover artists, particularly Tom Nikosey, who did 13 of our covers from RSVP4-16 and Brad Holland, who illustrated this years special 30th Anniversary cover. On the next 2 pages we've picked some of our favorite covers over the years as a special feature spotlighting these artists who have had so much to do with our success. Starting from the top left and continuing across the spread we want to give credit to these great illustrators. First line: Tom Nikosey/RSVP6, Cameron Eagle/RSVP23, Marvin Mattelson/RSVP18, Tom Nikosey/RSVP15, Gary Kelley/RSVP20, Valerie Sinclair/RSVP19 Second Line: C.F. Payne/RSVP24, Mark Fredrickson/RSVP17, Tom Nikosey/RSVP8, Tom Nikosey/RSVP5, Bill Mayer/RSVP.01, Tom Nikosey/RSVP16 Third Line: Tom White/RSVP.02, Francis Livingston/RSVP.04, John Jude Palencar/RSVP.03, Tom Nikosey/RSVP7, Kathleen Creighton/RSVP25 and Mel Odom/RSVP21.

Last, but not least, we would like to thank all the wonderful artists who have advertised with us over these 30 years, many over and over again. Without their support and involvement we couldn't have continued at such a high level for so long. And most of all the art directors, creative directors, designers and art buyers all over the U.S. and around the world who've used RSVP....our audience.

It's been a great ride.

CREDITS

Publishers Richard Lebenson and Kathleen Creighton
Coordination/Sales Richard Lebenson
Design and Promotion Kathleen Creighton, Bodkin Design
Business and Promotion Joe Greenstein
Traffic/Sales Frank Attong
Cover Illustration & Design Brad Holland
Website Design Art Imaging & CD-Rom Inc.
Typesetting/Design Emma Crawford
Thanks to Harvey Wilson, Ken Chung, Tom and Mary Chung, Martha Burton, Nancy Heinonen, George Dick, Frankie, Alex and the rest of the Pressmen and production staff of Everbest
Prepress Everbest/China, Fine Arts/Hong Kong
Printing Four Colour Imports Ltd and Everbest/China

CONTENTS

info@rsvpdirectory.com

www.rsvpdirectory.com

RSVP ONLINE

RSVP Online, our newest feature, has been getting rave reviews. Our book has always been one of the leading print resources for art buyers. Now, with RSVP Online, we have one of the best digital directories, as well. A special section of our web-site,

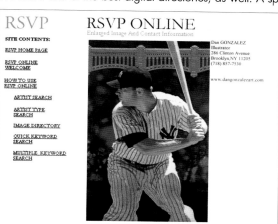

www.rsvpdirectory.com, RSVP Online is now one of the important places to visit on the web, with thousands of hits since its debut in February of 2001.

An illustrated listing of RSVP artists, past and present, this is fast growing into one of the most exciting, easiest to use, portfolio resources around. With RSVP Online you can access artists by name, type, or through single or multiple keyword categories. The most popular section of RSVP Online by far, is our Image Directory, where you can see all of the work in our database, alphabetically, 12 artists at a time. This way, you can view the entire database of images quickly and easily, if you wish. All these options feature a thumbnail image with click-on enlargement. These include all contact information including e-mail and a link to each artists own website (where available) to view more of their work. As an example, you can scan the Image Directory, find an artist you want to look at, click on the enlarged image and access their entire portfolio, if they have their own web-site, or contact them by sending them an e-mail directly from their listing!

With RSVP Online you now have all the advantages of instant access through the computer (in depth cross-referencing, frequently up-dated samples and access to the entire portfolio of hundreds of artists), along with the beautiful printing and immediacy of our book. This marriage of print and digital technology gives you an expanded ability to make the best choice for any assignment. Each on its own has some limitations, but together you really get the best of both worlds.

RSVP/ART IMAGING & CD-ROM WEB-PORTFOLIO SERVICE

Need a website? RSVP and Art Imaging can provide you with your own high-tec, digital web-portfolio for an unbelievably low price...and fast. You can find all the information regarding this service on our home page. Just click on the link. There are also some sample web-portfolios available as examples.

COVER ILLUSTRATOR
BRAD HOLLAND

Brad Holland is self-taught, and has been a professional artist since the age of 17. His drawings and paintings have appeared internationally, including covers and illustrations for *Playboy*, the Op-Ed section of the *NY Times*, *The New Yorker*, *Time*, *Newsweek*, *The Atlantic Monthly*, *The New York Times Magazine* and the *Frankfurter Allgemeine Magazine*. He's painted record album covers for Ray Charles, Stevie Ray Vaughn and Billy Joel and designed posters for the Odeon Theater in Vienna and the Yale Repertory Theater.

Brad has been called "an undisputed star of American Illustration" by the Washington Post. In 2000, we at RSVP voted him "the one artist who, in our opinion, has had the single greatest impact on the illustration field during the last 25 years". And critic Steve Heller summed up the first 20 years of Holland's career, saying that "Holland had radically changed the perception of illustration". He's been one of the most influential, independent and inventive artists of our time.

His work has been exhibited in museums around the world, most recently in 1999, a one-man retrospective at the Musee des Beaux Arts in Clermont-Ferrand, France. His paintings are in many corporate collections as well as the U.S. Library of Congress. Brad has won over 27 gold medals from organizations such as the Society of Illustrators, the Art Directors Club and the Society of Publication Designers, etc. He's been a writer, lecturer, animator and art director.

In 1999, Brad helped organize the First National Illustrators Conference in Santa Fe, New Mexico, where he was a featured speaker. This led to his role in helping to form the Illustrators Partnership of America, helping to organize artists as a group to collectively fight for their rights. In 2000 he was awarded the Walter Hortens Distinguished Service Award  from the Graphic Artists Guild in NY for his articles and speeches on the ill effects of stock illustration agencies on the freelance illustration business.

© Brad Holland

In October 2000 he was unanimously elected to the international design organization, Alliance Graphique International (AGI).

www.bradholland.net

RSVP's *CITYSCAPES* COMPETITION

Winners &

CITYSCAPES is the tenth annual theme competition sponsored by *RSVP: The Directory of Illustration & Design* and it drew hundreds of exciting and inventive entries from all across the U.S. and around the world. The four prize winners and 40 other finalists will be featured on RSVP's website at www.rsvpdirectory.com.

And the winners:

FIRST PRIZE: Halsted Hannah
$1250 plus a four-page color portfolio in RSVP.05 including 1000 card-stock reprints.

SECOND PRIZE: Francis Livingston
$750 plus a two-page color portfolio in RSVP.05 including 1000 card-stock reprints.

THIRD PRIZE: Kim Rosen
$300 plus a two-page color portfolio in RSVP.05 including 1000 card-stock reprints.

FOURTH PRIZE: Donato Giancola
$100 Honorarium

The competition's jurors were illustrators Roger Huyssen, Al Lorenz, Liz Lomax and William Low. Juror Alexis Seabrook was unable to attend the judging due to a scheduling conflict.

Second oldest of the national creative directories, RSVP has long been recognized for its dynamic approach to promotion, and for its encouragement of the creative use of contemporary illustration.

Finalists

The following Cityscapes finalists will also have their entries featured on the RSVP website at www.rsvpdirectory.com (Online Galleries section). Our congratulations to all of them for their fine work.

Nishan Akgulian
Patrick Arrasmith
Thomas Lee Bakofsky
Warren Beishir
Patrick Brickman •
Barry Brothers
William Carman
Eric Coleman
Carlo Cosentino •
Margaret Cusack
Larry Day •
Kenneth Dewey
Ingo Fas •
Nicole Gomez •

David Grove
Daniel Hauben
Greg Hergert •
Thomas Kidd
Hiro Kimura
Andy Lackow •
Ted Lewin
Daniel Lim
Gregory Manchess
Ewan MacLeish
Patrick Milbourn
Peter Pagano
Sandro Rodorigo
Rob Roper

Jim Salvati •
Ricardo Scozzari •
Gavin Spielman •
Mark Alan Stamaty
Michael Suh
Murray Tinkelman
Anthony Villany •
Neil Waldman
Adam Walko
Phil Wassell •
Eric Westbrook •
Alan Witschonke •

In addition to the winners and finalists, we also wanted to congratulate an excellent group of semi-finalists who also received honorable mention.

Yelena Balikov
Shawn Barber
Phil Bliss
Jason Branco
Priscilla Burris
Chris Buzelli
Rod Cameron
Stephanie Cooper •
Ray-Mel Cornelius
Frank Cusack
Stephan Daigle
Justin Davis•
Steven Dana
Michael DiCerbo
Eric Dinyer
Jim Effler
Michael Esposito
Chris Ferguson
Lindsay Fisher
Felipe Galindo

Barbara Garrison
Tom Graham
Nataliya Gurshman
Joan Hall
Donald Harvie
Steve Henry
Van Howell •
Brennan King •
Cecily Lang •
Lois Linet
Carol Luc
Kam Mak
Claudia McKinstry
Aaron Meshon
Gwyneth Morford
Michael Parker
Lynn Pauley
Tom Post
Gerardo Ramirez •
Jon Reinfurt

Irena Roman
Paul Ryan
Kim Schifino
Heather Sinclair
Chris Spollen
Emanuel Schongut
Phil Straub
Scott Thigpen
Mark Tocchet
Chris Tolivar
John Tomac •
Laura Vila
Oliver Yourke
Mark Wagner
Jesse Joshua Watson
James Allan Weyenberg •
Julia Woolf
Scott Zelazny
Bob Ziering •

• indicates artists appearing in this edition

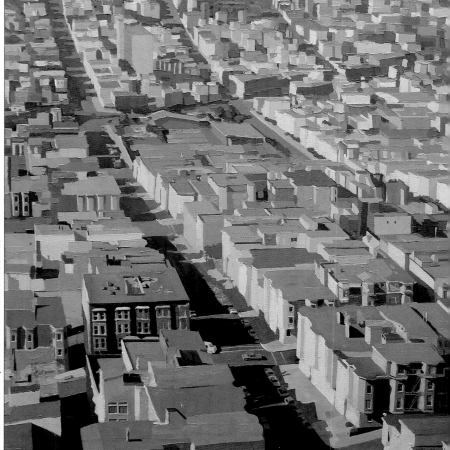

FIRST PLACE
HALSTED HANNAH

Halsted Hannah has been an illustrator and a painter for over three decades. A California native, he graduated from the California College of Arts & Crafts in 1981. He includes Ralph Steadman, Mark English, Sir Stanley Spencer, Barron Storey and Wayne Thiebaud among his many influences.

Hannah's work has ranged from editorial illustrations, cartoons, murals and story-boards, to graphic design and animation. His clients have included Warner Bros., Fox, Miramax, Hilton Hotels, Host Marriott, Coca-Cola, Pac Bell, Old Navy, Alka Seltzer, Reeses Pieces, Blockbuster, KFC, and the National Park Service. He was the recipient of a NewMedia INVISION gold medal award for his Web comic Snothartwig, a gold medal from the S.F. Society of Illustrators and the John Caples International Award.

More recently, Hannah has worked as a concept illustrator for a variety of clients including museums, zoos and corporate events around the world. Some of the projects have included Paul Allen's Experience Music Project in Seattle, the S.F. Giants/Coca-Cola attraction in SBC Park, Chicago's Museum of Science and Industry, Peoplesoft and the Black & White Ball in San Francisco, to name a few.

415.823.0843
www.halstedhannah.com

© Halsted Hannah

SECOND PLACE
FRANCIS LIVINGSTON

One of America's's top illustrators and painters for over 3 decades, Francis Livingston continues to turn out works of quiet beauty. Known as a painter of Southwestern scenes, his subjects also include urban imagery and still life. His work has been exhibited to wide acclaim all over the U.S.

Originally heavily influenced by Sargent, Whistler, Sloan and Hopper his work evolved into the color palette and light quality he is known for after seeing the work of the Impressionists and the Bay Area Figurative Movement, including Richard Diebenkorn, Wayne Thiebaud and others.

Mr. Livingston studied at the Rocky Mountain School of Art in Denver before moving to San Francisco to attend the Academy of Art. He later taught there for 10 years. He currently resides in Sun Valley, Idaho with his wife and two sons.

(208) 788-1978

© Francis Livingston

THIRD PLACE
KIM ROSEN

Kim worked as a graphic designer for several years before realizing that she was meant to be an illustrator. She received her BFA in Advertising Design from the Fashion Institute of Technology and an MFA Illustration degree from the Savannah College of Art and Design.

Her work combines traditional media such as painted textures, hand drawn patterns and intricate line work, with digital media, completing each illustration digitally.

Kim's list of clients includes CIO Magazine, EnRoute Magazine, Pohly & Partners, New York Daily News, Washington Post, Pennsylvania Gazette, Metropolitan Home Magazine, U.S. News and World Report, Wall Street Journal, Scholastic and YM.

She is represented by Anna Goodson Management Inc.
www.agoodson.com
info@agoodson.com.

(514) 983-9020

© Kim Rosen

ILLUSTRATION

LITTLE SHOP OF HORRORS

Mark Fredrickson

Tom Casmer

tel 941•359•8595

JERRY GONZALEZ DIGITAL ILLUSTRATION
JERRYTOONS.COM (917) 305-0800 OR (718) 204-8762

KADIR NELSON
8 8 8 . 3 1 0 . 3 2 2 2
www.kadirnelson.com

35

ILLUSTRATION. 314 PAVONIA AVE., JERSEY CITY N.J. 07302. (201) 798-6086

Member: Graphic Artists Guild

Jon Foster Studio

401-277-0880
jonfoster.com
alpine117@cox.net

© Dave Dorman

GUY BILLOUT

www.guybillout.com / guy@guybillout.com

©2004 Andy Lackow

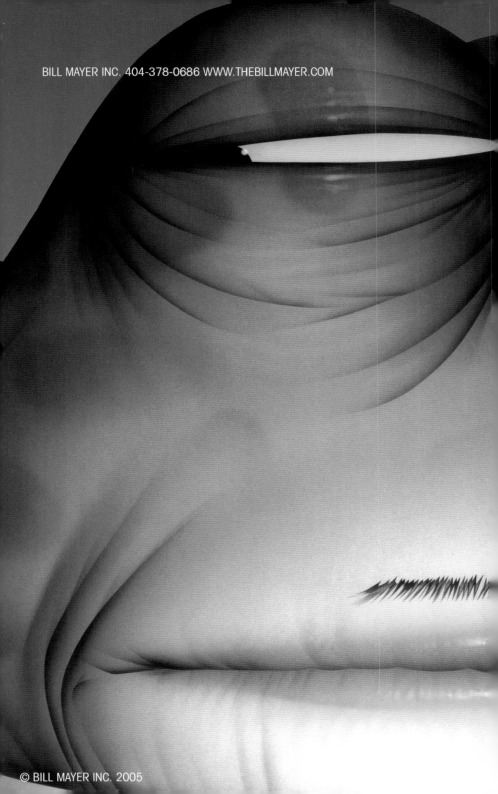

calder chism
humorous illustration · unflattering caricatures
775-530-0327

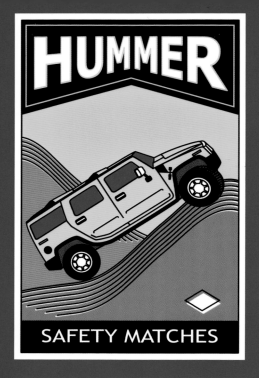

HUMMER

SAFETY MATCHES

FAST FOOD

SAFETY MATCHES

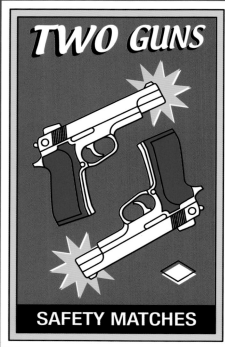

TWO GUNS

SAFETY MATCHES

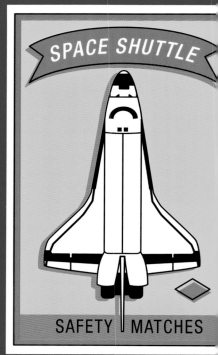

SPACE SHUTTLE

SAFETY MATCHES

Cyrus Deboo
44(0)208.788.8167   cyrus.deboo@virgin.net   www.cyrusdeboo.com

B.K. Taylor

24940 S. CROMWELL, FRANKLIN, MI 48025
(248) 626-8698   E-MAIL: T4XX@AOL.COM

COSENTINO
514·620·8912
www.carlocosentino.com

BB SAMS
HUMOROUS ILLUSTRATION
(770) 464-2956

ROB DUNLAVEY

Illustration

) 651-7503   www.bigillustrationgroup.com   www.robd.com

Original Site of
the Ford Motor Company
Detroit, Michigan

FORD MOTOR COMPANY

Henry Ford

Ford

STEPHEN HARRINGTON

255 WILTON ROAD WEST
RIDGEFIELD, CT 06877

(203)431-5854

E-MAIL:sharringtonillus
@earthlink.net

REPRESENTED BY
JOHN BREWSTER
CREATOIVE SERVICES

(203)226-4724

JOHN STEVEN GURNEY

710 Western Ave, Brattleboro, VT, 05301
802-258-2654 jsgurney@adelphia.net

Lane Yerkes Illustration

Tel: 239-561-1055 Fax: 239-561-1053
Cell: 239-634-2198 Email: Laneart45@cs.com

CLIFFORD FAUST

212-581-9461

cliffordfaust@yahoo.com

Jim Salvati
818-348-9012
Artist Rep.
818-224-0110
www.salvatidesign.com

Caitlin Kuhwald
www.caitlinkuhwald.com   caitlin@caitlinkuhwald.com
(5 1 0) 5 4 7 - 1 1 3 5

www
bradholland
net

Ron Sanders

Ron Sanders
Ron Sanders

history   romance   fantasy   adventure

E-mail
ron@sanders-studios.com

RSVP
Callback Answering Serv
(718) 857-9267

www.sanders-studios.com

he truth about tipping" - Golf Digest

dale stephanos
illustration

508-543-2500
www.dalestephanos.com

JOE KOVACH

(800) 355-1647 • (614) 939-1130

www.joekovach.com

barry shapiro 917-225-1231 www.barryshapiro.net

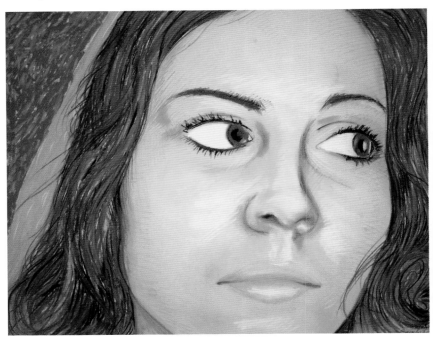

RSVP Callback Answering Service 718-857-9267

Richard Lebenson

253 WASHINGTON AVENUE, BROOKLYN, NY 11205
(718) 857-9267 E-MAIL: info@rsvpdirectory.com
WEB-SITE: www.richardlebenson.com

HERGERT

RSVP SPECIAL CALLBACK 718.857.9267

O.K. DOG
BeCAUSE
YOU CAN

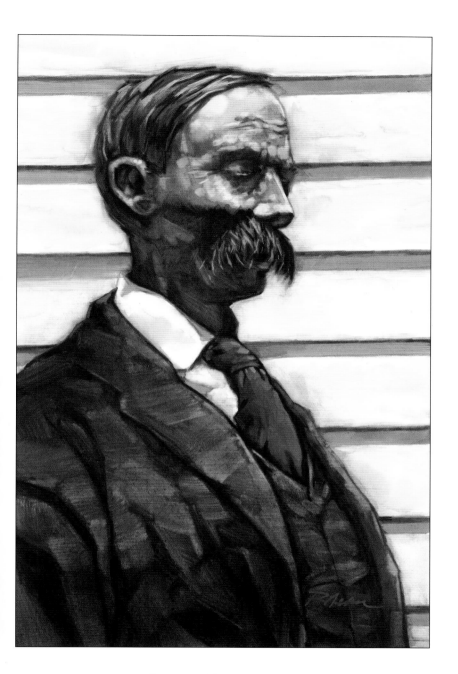

Russell Nelson

660.785.7332 | artwork@rlnelson.net | www.rlnelson.net

yvonnebuchanan.com

718-783-6682

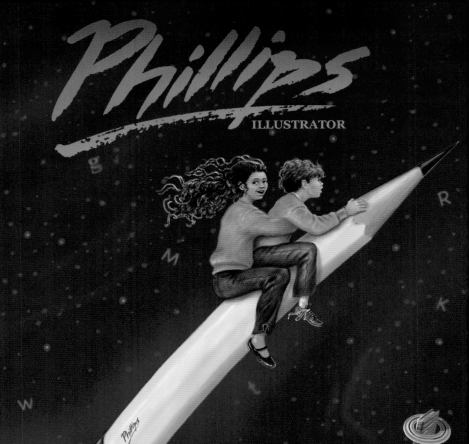

Phillips

ILLUSTRATOR

Gary Phillips
215-234-8231

garyphillipsstudio.com
garyphillips@garyphillipsstudo.com

Bob Ziering (212) 873-0034

bobziering@earthlink.net

RICK LOVELL

770.442.3943   www.ricklovell.com   rick@ricklovell.com

Lane duPont
203 222 1562
www.lanedupont.com

CHRIS SHEBAN   *Represented by Emily Inman*
312.836.9103
www.emilyinman.com

ANGELO

ARTIST/ILLUSTRATOR EXTRAORDINAIRE

764 Brady Avenue #233, Bronx, NY 10462 (718) 597-1275
RSVP CallBack Answering Service (718) 857-9267

emily **thompson**

5440 OLD EASTON ROAD DOYLESTOWN, PA 18901 215.766.3892 thompsonstudio@comcast
www.ethompsonstudio.com RSVP CALLBACK ANSWERING SERVICE 718.857.92

george **thompson**

0 OLD EASTON ROAD DOYLESTOWN, PA 18901 215.766.3892 thompsonstudio@comcast.net
w.thompsonillustration.com RSVP CALLBACK ANSWERING SERVICE 718.857.9267

CECILY LANG

336 WEST END AVENUE ◆ NEW YORK, NY 10023
TEL: (212) 580-3424 ◆ FAX: (212) 580-8526

202.965.0281   eric@ericwestbrook.com

Dave Dorman

850-651-5400

dormanart@yahoo.com

www.davedorman.com
www.wastedlands.com

George Schmidt

183 STEUBEN STREET, BROOKLYN, N.Y. 11205 (718) 857-1837
RSVP CALLBACK ANSWERING SERVICE (718) 857-9267

MIKE CRESSY

425.603.9669

www.mikecressy.com   mikecressy@earthlink.ne

ne (212) 772-7743   www.cathyhull.com
(212) 535-1877   chull@nyc.rr.com

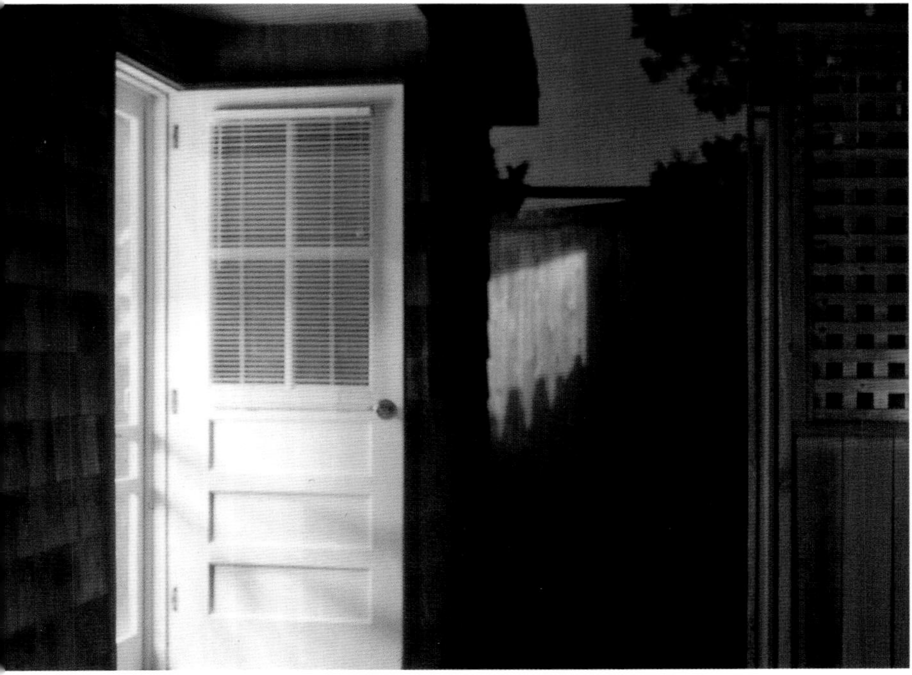

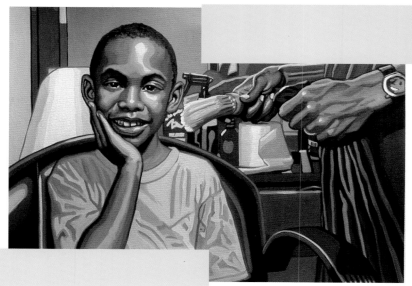

James Hoston Productions
420 Clinton Avenue Suite 2H
Brooklyn, New York 11238
(718) 230-7908
(718) 638-3548 Fax
Jhprod@nyc.rr.com

Larry Ross

973-377-6859
URL: www.larryross.net
Email: larry@larryross.net

DEAN LINDBERG
Fun, whimsical illustration and animation.

(612) 721-4993   www.deanlindberg.com   dean@deanlindberg.com

epresented By: Molly Birenbaum   203.453.9333
breps@sprintmail.com   fax: 203.453.1497

www.billthomson.com   Studio: 860.621.5501
billt140@cox.net   fax: 860.426.0631

Bruce Day

Illustrator

(208) 888-1944

FAX (208) 884-5003

brucedayink.com

Mía Bosna

345 Jug Hollow Road • Phoenixville, PA 19460 • 610.933.4545 • Mia.Bosna@Verizon.net

STUDIO

Ricardo Scozzari

818. 846.6814
e-mail: ricoact1@juno.com

CELEBRATING BLACK AUTHORS

JOHN MASON BREWER
1896-1975

ALAN WITSCHONKE
www.alanwitschonke.com   (617) 744-1930   alanwits@comcast.net

MIKE BIEGEL • FINE LINE ILLUSTRATION
888•267•2300 woodstock, vermont
www.mikebiegel.com • mike@mikebiegel.com • www.holidaycardsonline.com

LORETTA LUSTIG

330 CLINTON AVENUE, BROOKLYN, N.Y. 11205 (718) 789–2496

Barbara Garrison
12 East 87th Street, New York, NY 10128
TEL: (212) 348- 6382 FAX: (212) 423-9220
www.barbaragarrison.com

GET CO

Chris MacNeil
562.761.7946
www.cmacneil.com

Salzman International
415.285.8267
www.salzint.com

illustration sequential art character design

jon rea illustration

jonrea@jonrea.com
215.869.3497

rsvp callback 718.857.9267

www.jonrea.com

JON REA

Howard
Fine

914 948-9121

fax 914 948-9131

hrfine@optonline.net

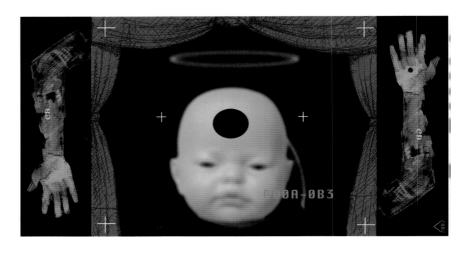

SERGIO CUAN

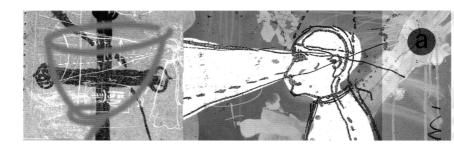

973.729.9112   e: slicuan@aol.com

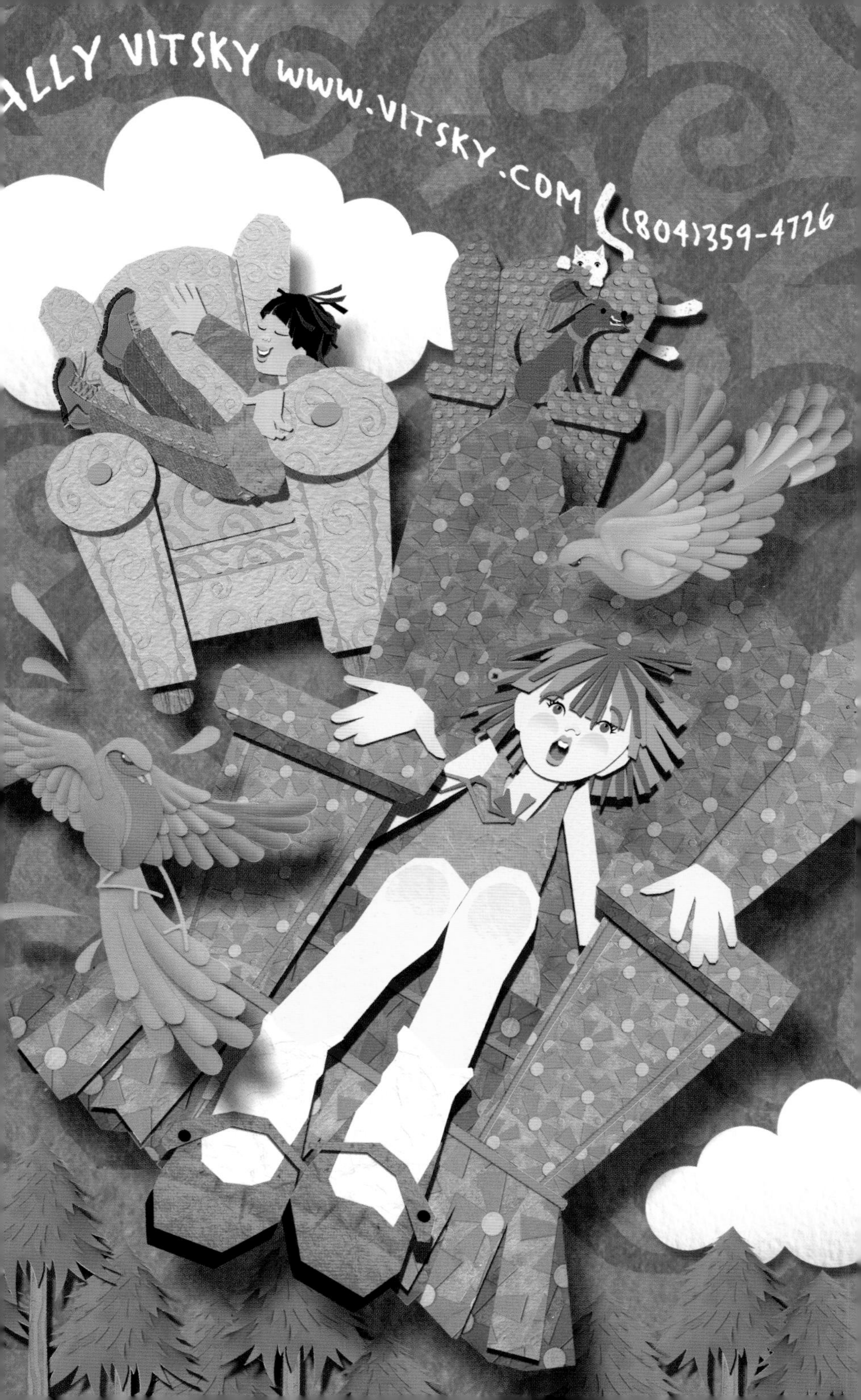
ALLY VITSKY WWW.VITSKY.COM (804)359-4726

PAUL YALOWITZ

RSVP CALLBACK ANSWERING SERVICE (718) 857-9267

Illustrations by Daniel Mascola

27 New Street, Hampton, NJ 08827 / 908-537-4884 / nofxmascola@yah

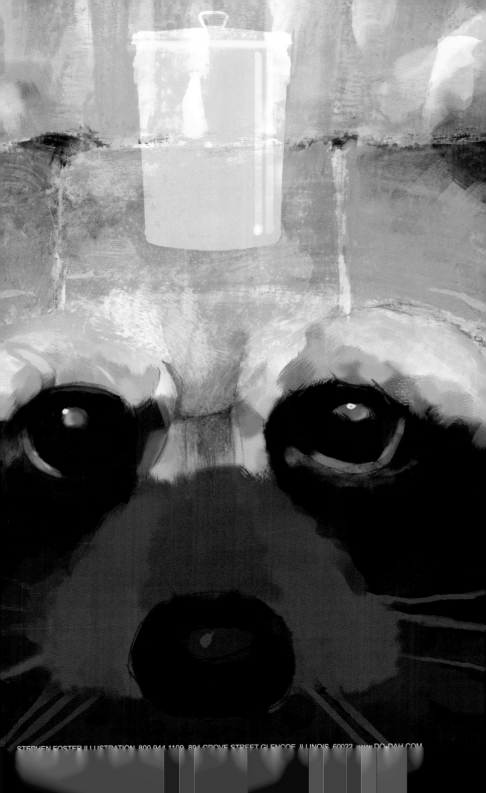

L SPECTOR • 860 355-5942 • fax 860 355-5370
ail: joelspectorillustration@charter.net
site: www.illustration-joelspector.com

Karol Kaminski

Jeremy & Nicole Tugeau   Artist Representatives

216.707.0854
www.tugeau2.com

ingo fast

120

718.387.9570

www.ingofast.com

jim hanson artist agent   312.337.7770

www.nelsonillustration.com
334.718.5994
gayle.nelson@earthlink.net

TIMOTHY WILSON

PHOTO ILLUSTRATION

387 2007   tw1982@juno.com   www.timothy-wilson.com

Travels with mom

Brennan King
www.brennanking.org   561.641.1780

Snarling Venus 40" x

Andy
Jurinko

(212) 732-3453

JEWISH
FUND FOR
JUSTICE

ZERO TOLERANCE
FOR POV

lynn foster illustration
9 1 7   3 0 1   4 9 5 2
http://altpick.com/lynnfoster

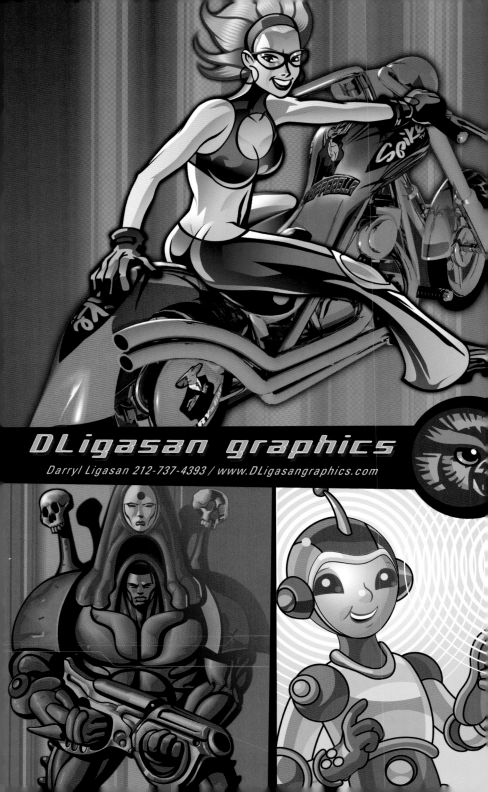

Food Affair Series

L i n k s

Personal

Happening

Awards

Contact

Clients

About

www.fernandacohen.com • rsvp@fernandacohen.com • Ph. 917.673.3447

MARY JANE BEGIN

401-247-7978
WWW.MARYJANEBEGIN.COM
MJBEGIN@COX.NET

133

Cameron Eagle
studio 405-621-5717

w w w . i n k r a n c h . c o m

DON DYEN

ILLUSTRATION
410 PARKVIEW WAY
NEWTOWN, PA 18940
(215) 968-9083
d.dyen@verizon.net

DANIEL J. STEGOS
(203)631-2897
Email: stegosart@hotmail.com

jason nobriga illustratio

808-381-9913 • WWW.JASONNOBRIGA.COM • JASON@JASONNOBRIGA.COM

SOCIETY OF ILLUSTRATORS 43
SOCIETY OF ILLUSTRATORS 44
SPECTRUM 6
SPECTRUM 7
SPECTRUM 8 GOLD AWARD "UNPUBLISHED" CATEGORY
SPECTRUM 9
RSVP "VIEW FROM THE EDGE" 2000 EXHIBITION
RSVP "SHADOWS" 2001 EXHIBITION

john howell

LOU M. POLLACK

Tele: **845.679.8508** or **888.448.2568**   E-mail: **lou@loulabelle.cc**

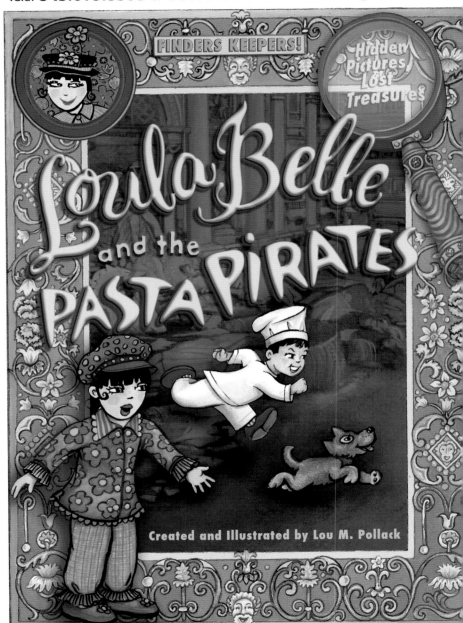

Let it Begin Here, Walker & Company, 2005

Christina A. Tugeau   757•221•0666

www.CATugeau.com

For Trade Books, contact Jane Feder (212) 532-6051

The Firekeeper's Son, Clarion B

Julie Downing

Christina A. Tugeau   757•221•0666

www.CATugeau.com

"The Truth About Twelve" - Published in 2004 by Boyds Mills Press

Christina A. Tugeau   757•221•0666

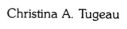

Cricket Magazine 2004

Christina A. Tugeau   757•221•0666

www.CATugeau.com

Stacy Schuett

Christina A. Tugeau 757•221•0666
www.CATugeau.com

ALPHA, BRAVO, CHARLIE, McElderry Books 2005

Mayday Mayday! McElderry Books 2004

Chris L. Demarest

Christina A. Tugeau  757·221·0666

www.CATugeau.com

Stop Teasing Taylor, Treasure Bay

Christina A. Tugeau 757•221•0666

www.CATugeau.com

Frank Sofo

Christina A. Tugeau 757•221•0666

www.CATugeau.com

Fred Willingham

Christina A. Tugeau 757•221•0666

www.CATugeau.com

RICHARD HARRINGTON

BARKING BEAGLE STUDIO

215.504.5850
BARKINGBEAGLESTUDIO.COM
BARKINGBEAGLE02@AOL.COM

DAN FIONE ILLUSTRATOR

Phone 215.699.7611   Fax 215.699.3644

penandinkalot@aol.com   www.danfione.com

SUBWAY
Styles

SUBWAY SKETCHING RULE #1: Unless you feel that you are completely inconspicuous (and to a

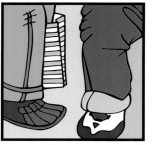  

any possible unpleasant confrontation) stick to drawing feet NOT faces.

JIM GALLAGHER

(908-236-8717)

Finding the Titanic

On it's maiden voyage on April 14, 1912, the *Titanic* struck an iceberg at full speed and sank within 3 hours. Over 1500 people lost their lives. Explorer Robert Ballard searched the sea floor using the coordinates from *Titanic's* distress calls and discovered the remains of the ill-fated ship in 1985.

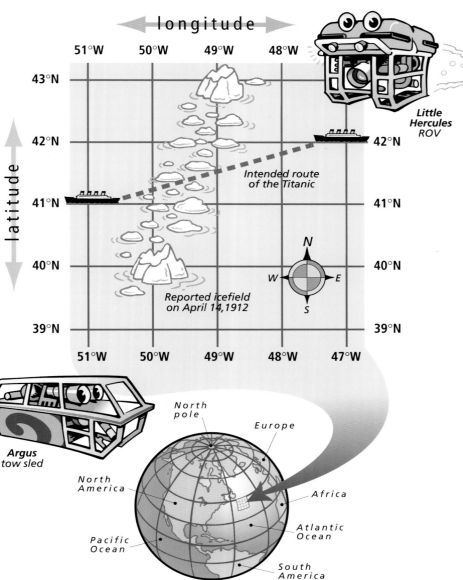

Phil Scheuer · Graphic Illustration · 212·620·0728
web: home.earthlink.net/~philscheuer

Michael Delaporte

www.Michaeldelaporte.com • 516.578.2446

Gavin Spielman   212 353 9127

www.Gavinart.com

LIZZY
ROCKWELL

www.lizzyrockwell.com

Tom Bennet

tombennettart.com

bennett@tombennettart.com

718-965-8460 917-913-5180

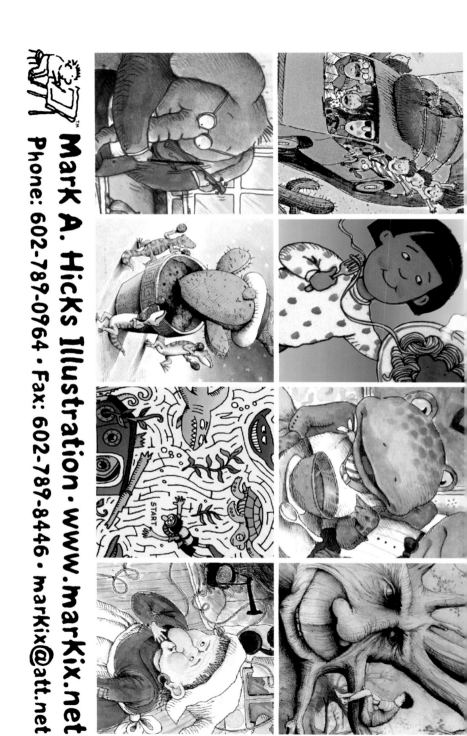

Mark A. Hicks Illustration · www.marKix.net

Phone: 602-789-0964 · Fax: 602-789-8446 · marKix@att.net

166

CATHY NOLAN
917-589-2387
Caricature Artist

www.cathynolan.com
cnolanart@hotmail.com

169

Erin Mauterer

New Jersey · (732) 922-2269
e: erin@erinm.com
www.erinm.com

SMEARY TALES

- *Highlights for Children*
- *Weekly Reader*
- *Quarasan!*

JOE CHIERCHIO

150 EAST 77TH STREET, NEW YORK, N.Y. 10021 (212) 772-1331

"Corporate Media Inc"

President Clinton
"Portfolio Graphics"

Editorial
Advertising
Corporate

"BBDO New York"

Laurent Linn

🖰 www.LaurentLinn.com
✉ contact@laurentlinn.com
New York City – 917.757.9863

LIZA R. PAPI

400 Chambers St. #6P, New York, NY 10282
646.414.8929 www.lizapapi.com

ean Keim Illustration • Graphic Design
(718) 783 – 0205 deankeim@hotmail.com
http://mysite.verizon.net/deankeim/index.html

ADAM GORDON · 718-238-7231 · email: ILLUSTRATES4U@AOL.COM
DIGITAL ILLUSTRATION

Santa's Express

LISA RIVARD

COLORADO 970-547-1630   lisa@rivardart.com
RSVP CALLBACK SERVICE (718) 857-9267

Debbie Dieneman

114 Vanderbilt Avenue, Brooklyn, NY 11205
(718) 875-1151, zoodraw@aol.com

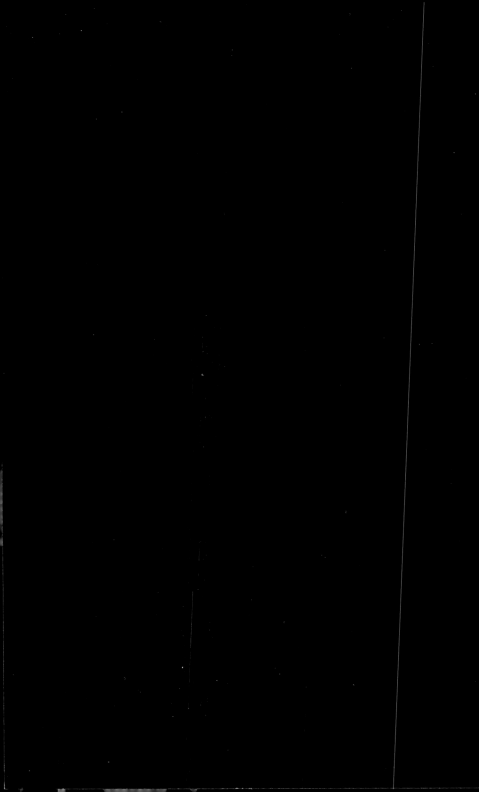

THE LAUNCHING PAD

For 30 years RSVP has been known for recognizing and promoting new talent. In fact, we've helped launch the careers of quite a few of today's top illustrators, many of whom did their first advertising in RSVP.

Continuing that tradition, The Launching Pad, one of our most popular features, has helped spotlight a new generation of America's best and brightest new talent. This year we're proud to introduce the work of another exciting, hand-picked group of young artists.

These are bright new professionals with fresh ideas, new techniques and often, a very different perspective on things. If you're looking for something a little different, you just may find it here.

This year's group includes the work of Chris Consul, winner of RSVP's annual Publication Award in the Society of Illustrators Student competition.

MACBETH

SAM WEBER
917.374.3373 | www.sampaints.com

Hoboken

Hoboken P

Antonio de Jesús

37 Van Reypen St, Jersey City, NJ 07306

917/ 826-8208

Elizardodejesus@hotmail.com

justindavis

one: 603.682.0526   email: drdavisj@mac.com   web: www.justinart.net

PHIL WASSELL

phone: 603-747-2119   email: thebfg88@hotmail.com

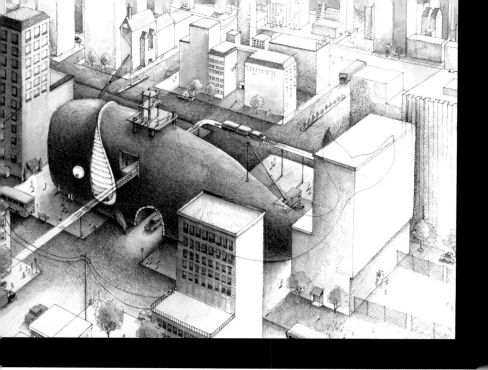

ATRICK J BRICKMAN

ickma@kent.edu   440. 946. 9910.   www.patrickbrickman.com

CHRIS CONSUL

CHILDREN'S BOOK ILLUSTRATIONS
(610) 291-1019 CCONSUL23@HOTMAIL.COM

CHRIS CONSUL

CHILDREN' BOOK ILLUSTRATIONS
(610) 291-1019   CCONSUL23@HOTMAIL.COM

www.rrallen.com

Raul Rodriguez Allen
ILLUSTRATION/DESIGN   RSVP Callback®   718 857 9267

Seth Baldwin

ail:thischarmngman@aol.com

phone:410-889-8666

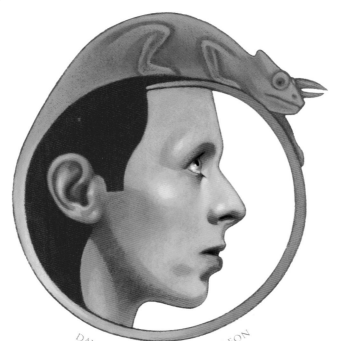

DAVID BOWIE THE CHAMELEON

CK CAVE   THE NOTORIOUS B.I.G.

HOLLY NEUBECK ILLUSTRATION

EB: HOLLYNEUBECK.COM   EMAIL: HOLLYNEUBECK@AOL.COM

corey a. parker
ILLUSTRATION
cp13national@yahoo.com

(616)-308-8364

phanie Cooper ——————————————————
5.638.0742 · stephanie@cooperillustrations.com · www.cooperillustrations.com

krista Wildermuth
phone: 973-568-0772
kristabear@earthlink.net
www.kristawildermuth.com

Laurie Grunin Illustration

gruninillustrations@yahoo.com
(508) 725-3557

1 Michael Drive
South Easton, MA 02375

607 . 280 . 7016
www.johnwtomac.com

GERARDO A. RAMIREZ
718 858 0473

NEOCITYSOL @ HOTMAIL.COM

Nicole Gomez

www.portfolios.com/NicoleGomez

gomazalia@yahoo.com

804.307.9527

DESIGN

RSVP

The Directory of Illustration and Design
30th Anniversary Edition

CARMINE VECCHIO • 203 241-3667
Logos, design and illustration impeccably craft

Graphic Design:

corporate/brand identity

Some journeys you go alone. Others are
collateral design
better with someone you can trust. Esta
packaging
persona le ayudará a evitar los peligros
information design
que no conoce bien para mostrarle vistas
book/editorial design
escondidas. Ou mieux, lesquelles vous
environmental design
avez déjà passé beaucoup de temps sans
type design
en voire. Assim é o lançamento de sua
multimedia and web
idéia no mercado: requer alguem que

entenda o conjunto de sua estratégia e,

que domine muito bem a profissão.

Wenn diese Person Ihre Sprache spricht,

umso besser! Ihre Idee hat eine Reise zu

machen. MasTypography Studio helps

you along the journey of that idea from

start to finish. We take you there and get

you back results.

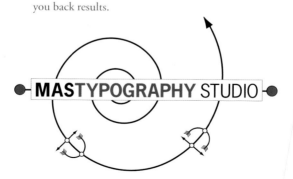

MASTYPOGRAPHY STUDIO

BROOKLYN, NY   (+1) 646 220-2816   WWW.MASTYPOGRAPHY.COM

207

the

LAMENTS

a novel

George Hagen

Random House Book Publishers

CAROLE MATTHEWS

THE Sweetest TABOO

Harper / Collins / Avon Book Publishers

BANANA
therapy

FOR DEPRESSION

FOR HANGOVERS

FOR NERVES

FOR BRAIN POWER

FOR BLOOD PRESSURE

FOR MORNING SICKNESS

FOR TEMPERATURE CONTROL

SEASONAL AFFECTIVE DISORDER

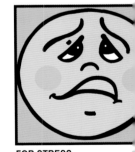

FOR STRESS

EMMA CRAWFORD
Graphic Design & Illustration
845.223.4816 ◆ 908.209.5552

ILLUSTRATION

The Directory of Illustration and Design
30th Anniversary Edition

Russ Spitkovsky
(718)-333-2265
198 Bay 28st. #2
Brooklyn, NY, 11214
email: russ@spitatart.com
Website: www.spitatart.com

troyhowellstudio

540 373 5199 / www.troyhowellstudio.com

BRUCE WALDMAN
18 WESTBROOK ROAD, WESTFIELD, NJ 07090
(908) 232-2840, RSVP CALLBACK ANSWERING SERVICE (718) 857-9267

477 3rd St. Apt. 3b Brooklyn NY 11215
bill@billalger.com
718.788.4840

LAURIE HARDEN·ILLUSTRATOR

LAURIE HARDEN, 121 BANTA LANE, BOONTON, NJ 07005 (973) 335-4578

C.F. PAYNE　　　212·223·9545

Lauren E. Simeone
Illustration from
The Garden State
609-426-4490
LESimeone@direcway.com

SIMEONE INK

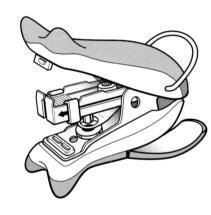

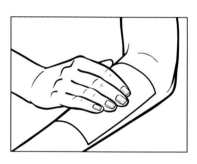

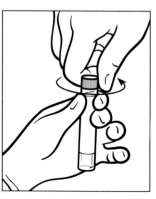

Francis Livingston

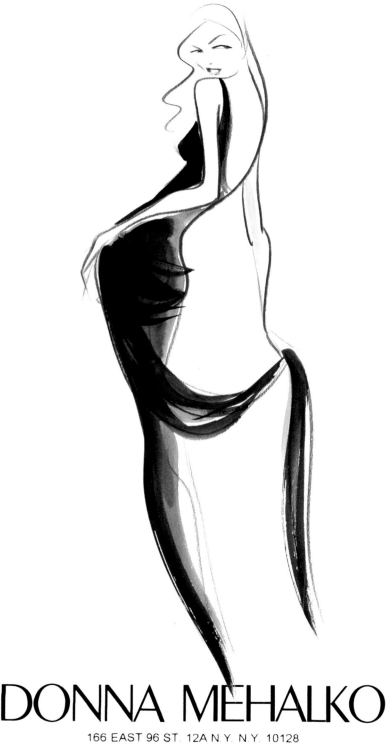

DONNA MEHALKO

166 EAST 96 ST. 12A N.Y. N.Y. 10128
212 534-1097

2002

Jim Gallagher

908-236-8717

Jim Gallagher

908-236-8717

JIM GALLAGHER

(908-236-8717)

JOHN LEAVITT

CARTOONIST – ILLUSTRATOR

WWW.JLEAVITT.NET
JLEAVITT@JLEAVITT.NET
(732) 991-4978

M.K. PERKER

917 - 507 - 9109
www.mkperker.com
600 W. 140th St. #9A

GERRY CLOUD
Illustration
CloudArtStudios®
717-284-2696
1189 Rawlinsville Road
New Providence PA 17560

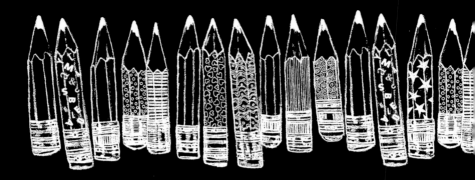

KAREN LEE

CONTEMPORARY
ART

(212) 865-2537

**220 WEST 107 ST.,# 2E
NEW YORK, N.Y. 10025**

Bill Gow / Graphic Design

601 Bound Brook Road, Suite 111, Middlesex, NJ 08846

voice: 732-424-8866
fax: 732-424-9696
www.studio1ne.com

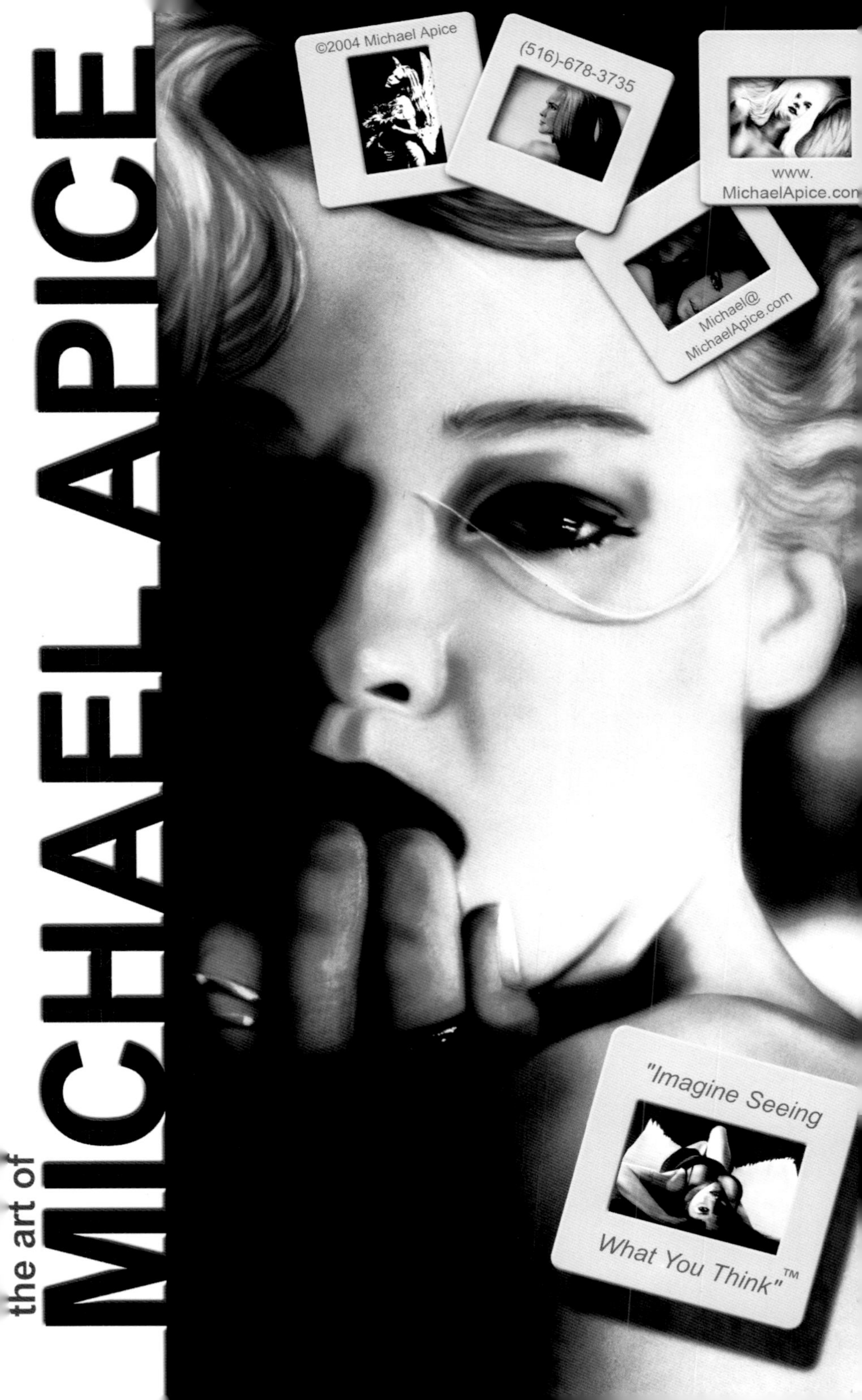
the art of
MICHAEL APICE
©2004 Michael Apice
(516)-678-3735
www.
MichaelApice.com
Michael@
MichaelApice.com
"Imagine Seeing
What You Think"™

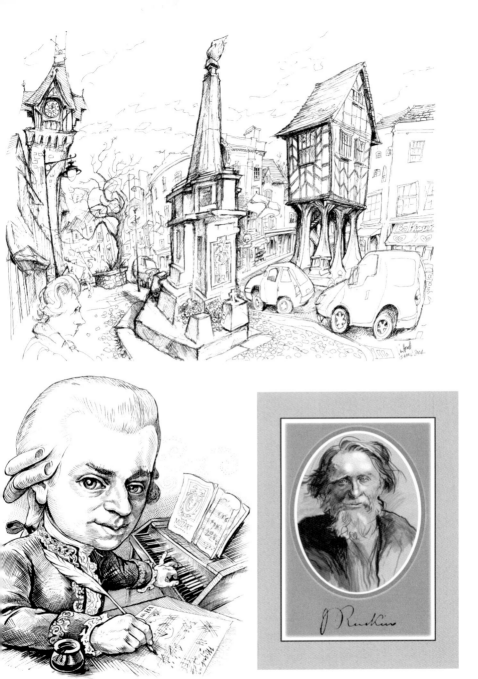

Van Howell

Email **vanhowell@writersartists.net**   Studio phone **011-44-208-341-9980**.
See **www.writersartists.net** for updated contact details, portfolio, and US client list.
Additional samples in all RSVP books since 1985, and at www.portfolio.com.

illustratio ns

by Lauren Simkin Berke
www.simkinberke.com
laurenberke@gmail.com

Eric Velasquez
ILLUSTRATOR
31 YALE ROAD, HARTSDALE, NY 10530 (914) 328-4988
EricVelasquez.Com

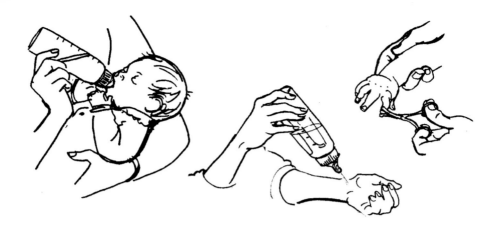

Betty Friedan

Wendy Wasserstein

IL Y A UN GESTE

Elizabeth Williams *Illustratio*
(212) 480-0887

Jennifer Caban

www.Mollycrabapple.com
Jen@Mollycrabapple.com
(917) 907 2150

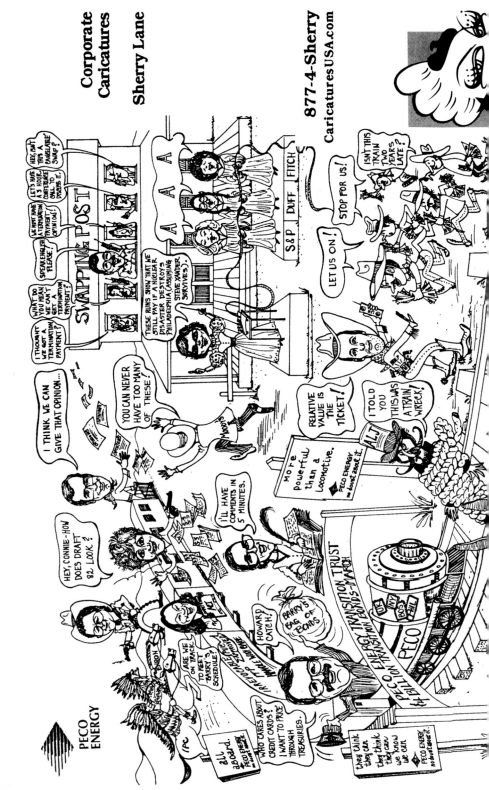

Corporate Caricatures

Sherry Lane

877-4-Sherry
CaricaturesUSA.com

INDEX

ILLUSTRATION

* RSVP Callback Answering Service (718) 857-9267

HARRISON Hugh 201.798.6086	36
HELTON David 423.622.3497	161
HERGERT Greg *	67
HICKS Mark A. 602.789.0964 FAX 602.789.8446	166
HOLLAND Brad www.bradholland.net	56,57
HOSTON Jim 718.238.7988	90
HOWELL John 510.7691421	141
HOWELL Troy 540.373.5199	217
HOWELL Van 011.44.208.341.9980	235
HULL Cathy 212.772.7743 FAX 212.535.1877	87
JANOVITZ Marilyn 212.727.8330	103
JURINKO Andy 212.732.3453	127
KAMINSKI Karol 216.707.0854	118
KEIM Dean 718.783.0205	175
KHUZAMI STUDIO 212.594.9396	125
KING Brennan 561.641.1780	124
KLEIN David G. 718.436.9666	63
KOVACH Joe 800.355.1647 614.939.1130	60
KUHWALD Caitlin 510.547.1135	55
LACKOW Andy 201.969.0080	39
LANE Sherry 877.4.Sherry	240
LANG Cecily 212.580.3424 FAX 212.580.8526	82
LEAVITT John 732.991.4978	229
LEBENSON Richard 718.857.9267	66
LEE Karen 212.865.2537	232
LIGASAN Darryl 212.737.4393	130
LINDBERG Dean 612.721.4993	94
LINN Laurent 917.757.9863	173
LIVINGSTON Francis 212.397.7330	223
LOVELL Rick 770.442.3943	74
LUSTIG Loretta 718.789.2496	101
MACNEIL Chris 562.761.7946 415.285.8267	104,105
MARTIN Richard 732.738.4838	119
MARTINI Angela 347.866.4238	156
MASCOLA Daniel 908.537.4884	114
MAUTERER Erin 732.922.2269	170
MAYER Bill 404.378.0686	40,41
MEHALKO Donna 212.534.1097	224
MICHLITSCH Ryan ryanmichlitsch@yahoo.com	194
NATALE Vince 845.679.0354	65
NELSON Gayle 334.718.5994	122
NELSON Kadir 888.310.3222	35

* RSVP Callback Answering Service (718) 857-9267

VAN METER Trevor 646.295.6750	61
VANN Bill 314.231.2322	42
VELASQUEZ Eric 914.328.1988	237
VILLANY Anthony 646.283.4683	91
VITSKY Sally 804.359.4726	111
WALDMAN Bruce 908.232.2840 *	218
WANG Qi 718.854.6795	216
WASSELL Phil 603.747.2119	188
WEBER Sam 917.374.3373	185
WESTBROOK Eric 202.965.0281	83
WEYENBERG James Allan 414.559.8943	31
WILDERMUTH Krista 973.568.0772	198
WILLIAMS Elizabeth 212.480.0887	238
WILLINGHAM Fred 757.221.0666	151
WILSON Timothy 636.387.2007	123
WITSCHONKE Alan 617.744.1930	99
YALOWITZ Paul *	112
YERKES Lane 239.561.1055 Cell 239.634.2198	52
ZIERING Bob 212.873.0034	72,73

THE LAUNCHING PAD

ALLEN Raul Rodriguez *	192
BALDWIN Seth 410.889.8666	193
BRICKMAN Patrick J. 440.946.9910	189
CONSUL Chris 610.291.1019	190,191
COOPER Stephanie 646.638.0742	197
DAVIS Justin 603.682.0526	187
DE JESUS Antonio 917.826.8208	186
GOMEZ Nicole 804.307.9527	202
GRUNIN Laurie 508.725.3557	199
MICHLITSCH Ryan ryanmichlitsch@yahoo.com	194
NEUBECK Holly hollyneubeck@aol.com	195
PARKER Corey 616.308.8364	196
RAMIREZ Gerardo 718.858.0473	201
TOMAC John W. 607.280.7016	200
WASSELL Phil 603.747.2119	188
WEBER Sam 917.374.3373	185
WILDERMUTH Krista 973.568.0772	198

3D ILLUSTRATION/DESIGN

CRAWFORD Emma 845.223.4816 908.209.5552   154,210
VITSKY Sally 804.359.4726   11
WILDERMUTH Krista 973.568.0772   198

COLLAGE

FAUST Clifford 212.581.9461   53
FOSTER Lynn 917.301.4952   129
JANOVITZ Marilyn 212.727.8330   103
LANG Cecily 212.580.3424 FAX 212.580.8526   82

SILHOUETTES, PAPER CUTS & CUT.OUTS

CRAWFORD Emma 845.223.4816 908.209.5552   154,210
FAUST Clifford 212.581.9461   53
VITSKY Sally 804.359.4726   111

WOODCUTS/SCRATCHBOARD/PRINTMAKING

DANZ David 530.622.3218   107
GARRISON Barbara 212.348.6382 FAX 212.423.9220   102
KLEIN David G. 718.436.9666   63
LEBENSON Richard 718.857.9267   66
SPITKOVSKY Russ 718.333.2265   214
WALDMAN Bruce 908.232.2840 *   218

CARTOONING/HUMOROUS

ALGER Bill 718.788.4840   219
ARNOLD Mike 973.275.5599 917.612.5540   165
BONO Peter 908.496.8524 CELL 908.268.2862   172
CHISM Calder 775.530.0327   43
COLON Terry 877.600.9667   136
CRESSY Mike 425.603.9669   86
DAY Bruce 208.888.1944 FAX 208.884.5003   96
EAGLE Cameron 405.621.5717   134,135
FAST Ingo 718.387.9570 312.337.7770   120,121
FREDRICKSON Mark 212.889.3337   29
FUJISAKI Tuko 800.208.2456 STUDIO 808.965.1314   62
GEARY Rick 619.234.0514 FAX 619.231.9035   225
GOLDBERG Richard A. 781.646.1041   68
GONZALEZ Jerry 917.305.0800 718.204.8762   34
GORDON Danny 405.728.1350   167
HALLGREN Gary 413.467.9805   126

CARICATURES

FASHION ILLUSTRATION/ACCESSORIES

TECHNICAL RENDERING & ILLUSTRATION

SCIENTIFIC/BOTANICAL/ZOOLOGICAL ILLUSTRATION

* RSVP Callback Answering Service (718) 857-9267

COMPUTER ART

ARTISTS REPRESENTATIVES

TUGEAU Christina 757.221.0666   143-151
TUGEAU 2 216.707.0854   118

GRAPHIC DESIGN
BODKIN CREATIVE 203.221.0404   211
CRAWFORD Emma 845-223-4816 908.209.5552   154,210
GOW Bill 732.424.8866 FAX 732.424.9696   233
KEIM Dean 718.783.0205   175
MASTYPOGRAPHY STUDIO 646.220.2816   207
NIKOSEY Tom 818.704.9993   208,209
VECCHIO Carmine 203.241.3667   206
WEYENBERG James Allan 414.559.8943   31

ART DIRECTION
BODKIN CREATIVE 203.221.0404   211
VECCHIO Carmine 203.241.3667   206

LETTERING, LOGOS & CALLIGRAPHY
VECCHIO Carmine 203.241.3667   206
BODKIN CREATIVE 203.221.0404   211
GOW Bill 732.424.8866 FAX 732.424.9696   233
HOWELL Van 011.44.208.341.9980   235
MASTYPOGRAPHY STUDIO 646.220.2816   207
NIKOSEY Tom 818.704.9993   208,209

PACKAGE DESIGN
BODKIN CREATIVE 203.221.0404   211
CRAWFORD Emma 845.223.4816 908.209.5552   154,210

COSTUME DESIGN
CRAWFORD Emma 845.223.4816 908.209.5552   154,210

DOLLMAKING/EXHIBIT/DISPLAY/PROPS
CRAWFORD Emma 845.223.4816 908.209.5552   154,210

PHOTOGRAPHY/HAND.PAINTED PHOTOGRAPHY
CREIGHTON Kathleen 718.636.1111   88,89
GREENSTEIN Joe 718.636.9535   113
VILLANY Anthony 646.283.4683   91
WILSON Timothy 636.387.2007   123

* RSVP Callback Answering Service (718) 857-9267

Mark Summers
will draw your portrait for free
when you join the
SOCIETY OF ILLUSTRATORS

Steven Stroud, SI President 1995-1998   by Mark Summers

Right after you volunteer for several committees, hang a bunch of shows,
get appointed to the board of directors, chair those committees
you volunteered for, serve on the Executive Board, and,
oh yes, become President.
Between now and then you can have a lot of fun.

Contact the Society for membership information,
or visit our website for an application.

128 East 63rd Street
New York, NY 10021-7303
212.838.2560 • fax.2561
www.societyillustrators.org
EMail:si1901@aol.com

Founded February 1, 1901

PROTECTION

STANDARDS

ETHICS

ADVOCACY

INFLUENCE

PEER NETWORK

INSURANCE

UNION CLOUT

KNOWLEDGE

RESPECT

SUPPORT

JUST A FEW OF THE BIG DIVIDENDS
FROM A SMALL INVESTMENT
IN YOUR FUTURE.

JOIN US AND REAP THE REWARDS.

THE GRAPHIC ARTISTS GUILD

1-800-500-2672

JOIN ON LINE...
WWW.GAG.ORG

Have you seen RSVP Online yet?

You can see it on our website,
www.rsvpdirectory.com.